Once upon a time...

"Portrait of Love"

This is where the wealthy
And the powerful rule.
It is her world —
A world apart from mine.

Her name is Catherine.

From the moment I saw her
She captured my heart
With her beauty,
Her warmth
And her courage.
I knew then,
As I know now,
She would change
My life forever!

He comes from a secret place
Far below the city streets —
Hiding his face from strangers
Safe from hate and harm.
He brought me there
To save my life.
And now, wherever I go,
He is with me in spirit
For we have a bond
Stronger than friendship —
Or love.
And although we cannot
Be together —
We will never
Ever
Be apart.

CATHERINE HURRIES THE CHILDREN OUT, PRAYING THAT THIS EVENING'S TERROR WILL QUICKLY FADE.

AND--TRUSTING IN HER SAVIOR--REASSURES THEM AGAIN THAT THEIR FATHER IS NOT DEAD.

BUT LONG BEFORE HORTON CAN RECOVER, DEBRA AND HER CHILDREN WILL BE SAFELY AWAY AND BEGINNING THEIR NEW LIFE.

MOMENTS BEFORE, HE FELT CATHERINE'S FEAR. NOW HE FEELS ONLY RELIEF--

--AND LOVE.

SIRENS!

I CAN MANAGE. GO!

ONCE AGAIN SHE MUST INVENT AN EXPLANATION THAT WILL SATISFY THE POLICE--AND HER ASSOCIATES AT THE D.A.'S OFFICE AS WELL.

FOR THERE IS A SECRET... AND A RENDEZVOUS... AND SHE IS SWORN TO KEEP BOTH.

IT'S ALWAYS A PRIVILEGE TO WATCH YOU WORK, ELIZABETH.

YOUR COLORS AND SHAPES ARE MORE ELOQUENT THAN ANY WORDS.

I-I ENVY YOU.

WHY, CHILD! YOU HAVE IT IN YOU TOO.

WHEN YOU WERE A BOY THE DRAWINGS YOU BROUGHT ME WERE MORE THAN PROMISING. I TOLD FATHER SO.

YOU JUST NEEDED A FIRE LIT UNDER YOU. NOW, LOOK AT THAT NASTY WHITE SPACE. HOW HUNGRY IT IS!

DON'T YOU SEE SOMETHING THERE? SOMETHING THAT COULD ONLY BE SAID WITH A BRUSH?

I SEE AN EXPANSE, VAST AND INTIMIDATING AS THE MOON'S WIDEST PLAIN. HOW WOULD I BEGIN...?

BY KNOWING WHAT SETS YOU ON FIRE!

MOUSE KNOWS *CHUCKLE*

BUT...IS IT POSSIBLE?

THAT CANVAS HOLDS NOTHING BUT POSSIBILITIES! ALL YOUR FEARS AND ALL YOUR DREAMS ARE THERE.

QUICK! WHAT DO YOU SEE?

CATHERINE!

THANK YOU, ELIZABETH. I ONLY HOPE--

SHH! DON'T TALK YOURSELF OUT OF IT. GO! TAKE THE RISK. SHOO!

OOPS! WELL... THINK OF IT AS WAR PAINT, CHILD.

SEE YOU, VINCENT!

REMEMBER, ONCE YOU START, YOU MUST FINISH! LET ME KNOW HOW THE BATTLE GOES.

HOURS LATER...

THE REPEATED SOUND OF PAPER BEING TORN AND CRUMPLED ABRUPTLY STOPS.

AND VINCENT'S CHAMBER RUMBLES WITH A GROWL--A GENUINE GROWL--OF DISGUST.

THE BATTLE GOES POORLY, ELIZABETH. THE ENEMY IS STRONG. CATHERINE'S IMAGE LIVES IN MY HEART. BUT ON PAPER HER EYES ARE DEAD! WHY?

-- SEEKING SOLACE IN FATHER'S CORNUCOPIAN LIBRARY.

Aided by words and pictures, Vincent's youthful imagination carried him to the great forbidden places of the world above.

Now something more than a man, still vulnerable to the top-dwellers' blind fears, he continues to dream in his candlelit prison. But the books, his doors to the sun, are always there.

His fingers roam the frayed bindings of revered tomes -- and suddenly close on an aged, unpublished journal.

JOHN PATER...!

The yellowed pages are filled with aggressively precise script. It is the handwriting of a genius, a visionary...a demagogue.

Several hours pass unnoticed...

"...IS AT BEST MISGUIDED, AT WORST A SELF-DEFEATING FOOL TO SEEK AID AND INSPIRATION FROM HIS FELLOW MAN.

SUCH JOURNEYS OF CREATION CAN ONLY BE MADE ALONE--"

"--APART EVEN FROM LIKE-MINDED OTHERS."

I KNOW THAT PASSAGE. I'VE READ IT BEFORE WITH SORROW AND REGRET. BUT YOUR VOICE CAN MAKE EVEN THOSE WORDS SEEM UPLIFTING.

WORD OF HIS LEAVING SINGS THROUGH THE PIPES. BENEATH HIS FRIEND'S WELL-WISHES HE HEARS THEIR FEAR, THEIR DEPENDENCE ON HIM--SAD REMINDERS THAT NO PARADISE IS WITHOUT ITS SERPENTS.

IN THE WHISPERING GALLERY, WHERE THE ROCK WALLS DIVIDING ONE WORLD FROM THE OTHER ARE THINNEST, SOUNDS AND VOICES SEEP THROUGH FROM ABOVE.

I FEEL CLOSE TO CATHERINE HERE. COMFORT AND SAFETY CALL ME TO STAY.

NO! I MUST GO FARTHER, MUCH FARTHER AWAY.

THE NETWORK OF MAN-MADE TUNNELS GIVES WAY TO SPLENDID NATURAL CAVERNS--ALL FAMILIAR HAUNTS--ALL PLACES HE HAS SHOWN CATHERINE, AS A PRINCE MIGHT SHOW HIS PRIVATE TREASURE-HOLD TO HIS CHOSEN LOVE.

EVERY STONE, FOUNTAIN AND FILTERING STREAM OF LIGHT REMINDS HIM OF SOME SHARED EXPERIENCE WITH HER.

BUT LITTLE MORE THAN A YEAR AGO, THE LOVE WHICH GAVE RISE TO THOSE MEMORIES DID NOT YET EXIST.

HE FOUND HER ONE NIGHT IN THE PARK, SLASHED AND LEFT BLEEDING TO DEATH BY THUGS WHOM HE LATER REPAYED IN KIND.

OUT OF COMPASSION HE CARRIED THE UNKNOWN YOUNG WOMAN DOWN TO HIS SECRET WORLD.

FOR DAYS AFTERWARD, DESPITE FATHER'S MISGIVINGS, VINCENT TENDED HER INJURIES--

--SOOTHED HER PAIN WITH READING AND GENTLE CONVER-SATION, AND-- UNTHINKABLY-- FELL IN LOVE.

CATHERINE, TOO, WAS CAPTIVATED BY HIS VOICE, BY HIS TENDERNESS AND STRENGTH, BUT WHEN THE REVELA-TION CAME--

MY FACE! OH GOD! OH GOD, NO!

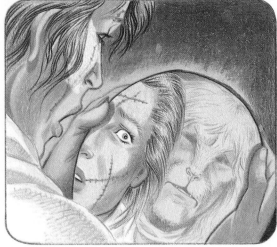

I MUST SIMPLY GET OUT OF THE WAY AND LET MY HEART PAINT IT!

THIS IS THE PLACE HE HAS BEEN SEEKING.

WELL, ELIZABETH... LET'S SEE WHAT RISES FROM THE FIRE.

THE TRICKLING SOUND OF A SMALL WATERFALL INVITES HIM TOWARD A SHALLOW CAVE. IT DRAWS HIM WITHIN. IT FEELS RIGHT.

BRUSH POISED, THE ARTIST FACES HIS ADVERSARY.

WHO'S THERE?

SO HE HAS DE EARS OF A CAT TOO? HEH HEH HEH.

MAYBE NOT. DE OLD CRAZY WOMAN WALKS HEAVY DESE DAYS.

NARCISSA!

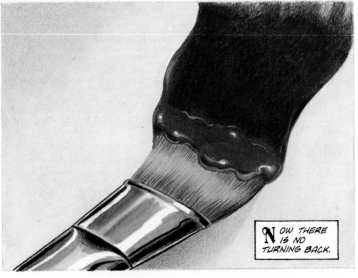

CHOKE

WHA--? WHAT WAS THAT? MOUSE? WAS THAT YOU?

MOUSE...?

OH, MY GOD...

CATHERINE...!

AND MORE...

MY DEAR MARGARET...I... WHEN YOU LOVE SOMEONE THAT MUCH, YOU NEVER REALLY LOSE THEM.

VINCENT'S MADE CATHERINE LIVE FOREVER.

THAT SAME MOMENT, A WORLD AWAY...

THE GOLDEN BLANKET OF EVENING SETTLES OVER CENTRAL PARK. THE NIGHT PROMISES TO BE UNUSUALLY WARM FOR EARLY SPRING.

PERHAPS HE WILL COME TO HER BALCONY TONIGHT.

HAVING MADE THE RARE DECISION NOT TO WORK LATE AT THE OFFICE, CATHERINE ALLOWS HER LAST TRACE OF GUILT TO EVAPORATE--ALONG WITH THE DAMPNESS IN HER FRESHLY-WASHED HAIR.

IN THE HUM OF RUSH HOUR TRAFFIC SHE HEARS, IT SEEMS, AN EXPECTANT NOTE.

SHE IS NOT AN EMPATH, AS HE IS--

--BUT SOMETIMES THERE ARE... FLASHES OF... INTUITION.

NO, HE WILL NOT COME TO HER. SHE MUST GO TO HIM!

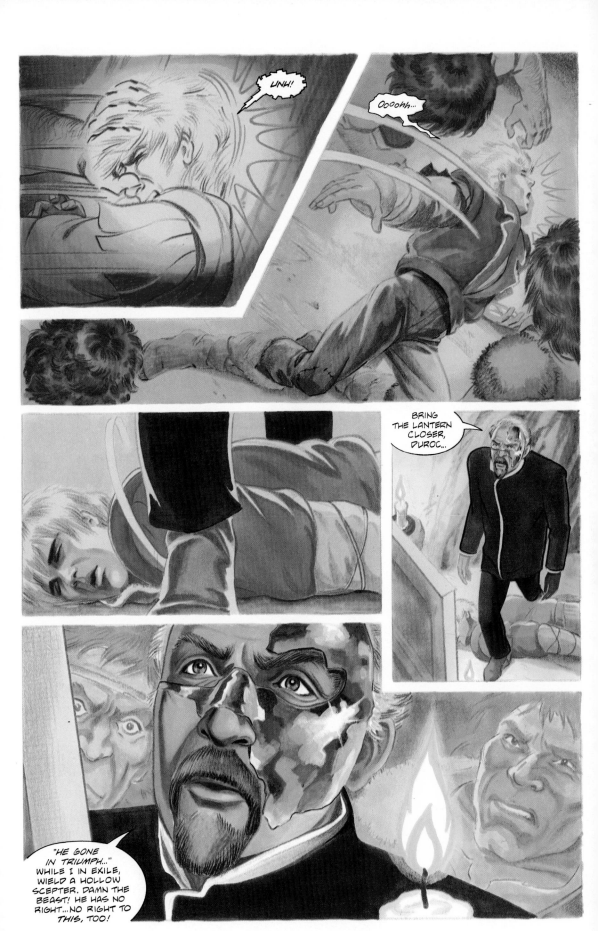

LATER...

EXAGGERATING? HUH! I'VE SCARCELY SAID ENOUGH! WHY, YOU'VE GIVEN OUR WORLD ITS OWN "GINEVERA DE'BENCI," ITS OWN "MONA L--"

--NOW, CONTENT AS I AM, FATHER, THAT'S GOING MUCH TOO FAR!

WELL, WE'LL LET THE REAL EXPERTS DECIDE!

THERE THEY ARE! HEY! WE MADE LOTS BETTER TIME THAN YOU TWO DID!

BLAME THIS OLD HIP OF MINE, JAMIE. CATHERINE! I'M SO GLAD TO SEE YOU.

REMEMBERING THE MANY MONTHS IT TOOK TO EARN FATHER'S TRUST, SHE SMILES... AND QUIETLY EMBRACES HIS SON.

VINCENT...

SLOWLY, SHYLY, HIS POWERFUL ARMS ENFOLD HER.

THIS IS...COLORFUL?! I'M ALMOST AFRAID TO ASK--

--SOMETHING HAS HAPPENED, CATHERINE...SOMETHING WONDERFUL. WILL YOU COME AND LET US SHARE IT WITH YOU?

OF... COURSE.

SHE IS BOTH LOST AND FOUND IN HIS GAZE.

AND SO ITS TRUTH IS UNIVERSAL, MEANT TO BE SHARED BY ALL, EH? YOU ARE INDEED JACOB'S SON--

--BUT YOU MIGHT HAVE BEEN MINE.

I FEEL FOR YOU, VINCENT, TRULY. WHO KNOWS BETTER THAN I THE BITTER PAIN OF THE *OUTCAST*? WE ARE ALIKE, REACHING FOR FORBIDDEN FRUIT.

BUT JOIN ME AND YOU SHALL *TAKE* THE WOMAN OF YOUR DESIRE--

NO...ALL THAT HAS EVER TOUCHED MY SOUL IS IN THAT PORTRAIT-- EVEN *YOU*.

--EVEN AS I *RECLAIM* THE WORLD I BUILT, THE WORLD THAT SHOULD *ALWAYS* HAVE BEEN MINE.

IN THE WORLD YOU WOULD MAKE, WE'D ALL BE AS YOUR BRUTE-MEN. THERE WOULD BE NO LOVE... AND NO REASON FOR ART.

tsk YOU LACK VISION AFTER ALL. IT IS SAID THAT, GIVEN INFINITE TIME AND AN ENDLESS SUPPLY OF TYPEWRITERS, A CHIMPANZEE WILL RECREATE SHAKESPEARE.

CLEARLY, YOUR SINGLE WORK OF GENIUS IS NO MORE THAN A RANDOM ACCIDENT. BUT, EVEN SO, I WILL *NOT* PART WITH IT--

--WITHOUT A *FIGHT*.

--IT IS LOVE.

THAT'S HOW HE SEES ME...?

OH, GOD... I NEVER THOUGHT THAT...

JOHN PATER, TOO, SEES AND UNDERSTANDS.

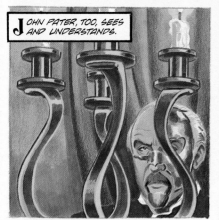

IT IS EVERYTHING THAT HE DOES NOT-- AND CAN NEVER--POSSESS.

A F T E R W O R D

Beauty and the Beast has been an extraordinary experience for all of us — a convergence of many talented people who went on an adventure together.

The original concept for the series was based on a number of different ideas. Kim LeMasters, head of CBS programming, had seen Jean Cocteau's 1945 film of *Beauty and the Beast*. He approached Paul Witt and Tony Thomas, with whom I'd been working. LeMasters wondered if there was some way that we could do a modern version of the story for television. At the same time, I had been searching for a way to tell a classical love story in contemporary terms, or a contemporary love story in classical terms. Great love stories require an epic obstacle in the path of the lovers, and LeMasters' interest in Cocteau's film dovetailed with what I'd been thinking about. In our love story, Vincent's "otherness" became the obstacle in the path toward union.

Using underground tunnels as a setting, however, was an idea I'd been holding in my mind since reading a series of articles about people living in the steam tunnels below the Waldorf Astoria in New York. I had done some research and discovered that there are nearly *three hundred miles* of man-made tunnels beneath Manhattan. Constructed around the turn of the century, most are uncharted and forgotten and, since Manhattan is built on bedrock, there are natural caves, subterranean caverns, even underground rivers, below the city as well. The notion of vast areas of unknown territory just beneath the streets of New York intrigued me. I had wanted to do something with those tunnels and it was the perfect setting for Vincent's almost magical, hidden world.

We truly had no idea of how the show would be received. Admittedly, a relationship between a woman from the upper East Side of Manhattan and a creature who lives in a mythical world below the city is an odd premise for a television series. How would the audience react to something so different from standard programing?

We were staggered. The viewer response from viewers to *Beauty and the Beast* has been tremendously heartening. The series seems to strike a very deep chord — partly, I think, due to the power of the myth itself, and partly due to our ambitions to tell stories with great depth of feeling.

As the series unfolds, our challenge is to continue to push the limits of narrative storytelling on television and to explore a relationship that has never been seen on television before. In many ways the story of Catherine and Vincent is still evolving, and we are following it just as much as we are writing it. One of the joys of this project is that, from week to week, the show can be about anything it wants to be about. There is much room for experimentation, and though we have an overall direction to the series, within that direction is a tremendous amount of creative leeway. One episode may be all action, the next could be something highly dramatic or intensely personal: big stories and little stories.

As for the choice of the two actors to play the lovers, we agreed, almost from the outset, that Ron Perlman should play Vincent. While the character may look like a beast, he is all feeling and emotion. We wanted an actor who would be able to transcend his make-up. And Ron Perlman is an actor's actor.

For Catherine... I had long admired the work of Linda Hamilton. Seeing her performance in *The Terminator*, I knew she was an actress who could portray a woman of great strength, a woman in transition, a woman of compassion.

We're blessed to have so many gifted people working together, people who continue to be stimulated and excited by the on-going adventure of creating the show each week. It's one of those rare experiences; and remarkable things have come out of it.

I'd like to thank *Beauty and the Beast's* many fans. They are an extraordinary group of intelligent and literate people whose support for the show has encouraged all of us from the first night we went on the air. I am quite proud of this graphic novel. Translating from one medium to another is always difficult, and Wendy Pini has done a remarkable job. Her artwork and story capture the spirit of *Beauty and the Beast* very deeply, very powerfully...

Ron Koslow
May 1989

B I O G R A P H Y

Wendy Pini was born Wendy Fletcher in Gilroy, California. Gilroy is known as "The Garlic Capital of the World" — a reputation guaranteed to foster escapism — and it is not surprising that at an early age Wendy turned in the direction of fantasy. With the inspiration of Shakespeare, Rackham, Kipling, Disney, Ozamu Tezuka, Chuck Jones, among many others, she began applying pencil and crayon to any convenient surface, spinning her own tales of elves and monkey-gods, aliens and sorcerers.

Wendy began exhibiting her artwork in fanzines and at science fiction conventions in the mid-1960s, garnering awards and recognition. In 1972 she married Richard Pini and, two years later, began her professional career as an illustrator for science fiction magazines such as *Galaxy* and *Worlds of If*. She provided covers and interior art for about three years, until a project called *Elfquest* beckoned in 1977. As the first continuing fantasy/adventure series to be created, written, and illustrated by a woman, *Elfquest* became a phenomenon in the industry, appealing to comics and fantasy/science fiction readers alike.

While *Elfquest* has been an ongoing work for over ten years, it has not been Wendy's only focus. She has also done work for Marvel and DC Comics, co-written the novel *Journey to Sorrow's End* with her husband/editor Richard, and supplied the text and illustrations for *Law and Chaos*, an art book inspired by the writings of Michael Moorcock. Now that *Elfquest*'s second "mega-chapter," *Siege at Blue Mountain*, has been completed Wendy is turning her sights in other directions: stage acting and book illustration. *Portrait of Love* is her latest labor of love. There will be more.

Photo by Richard Pini

Wendy Pini

Olivia De Berardinis is an artist with a deep, vibrant feeling for the feminine form. The determined elegance of her approach, with its boldness, and reality within traditional fantasy, celebrates the essential ego and libido of mankind.

Olivia was born in California in 1948 and was raised on the eastern seaboard. In 1966, she went to New York to attend the School of Visual Arts. Only recently she moved her studio from New York to Los Angeles. Olivia's technical virtuosity includes works in pencil, gouache, pastel, acrylic, oils and watercolors, utilizing brush and airbrush. Olivia's artwork has been seen in periodicals world-wide, and she is a regular contributor to *Playboy* magazine.

The pencil sketches on these pages were done by Wendy Pini on the set of *Beauty and the Beast* as part of her preliminary work for *"Portrait of Love."*

Ron Perlman stars as Vincent, the powerful man/beast whose appearance belies his intelligence and nobility.

Born in Manhattan on April 1, 1950, Perlman is the son of a jazz drummer who played with Artie Shaw's band before leaving the profession. Perlman began performing in high school, first as a comedian, then as an actor. He continued acting while at the New York City University and while earning a Master of Fine Arts degree at the University of Minnesota. After returning to New York he joined the Classic Stage Company and performed with them for two years, when Tom O'Horgan, director of Broadway's *"Hair,"* cast him in the highly successful off-Broadway *"The Architect and the Emperor of Assyria."* Perlman went on to star in numerous New York and regional theater productions including *"Tartuffe," "The Iceman Cometh," "House of Blue Leaves,"* and *"Pal Joey."*

Perlman's portrayal of Vincent earned him an Emmy Award nomination for Outstanding Lead Actor in a Drama Series in 1988, and was voted Best Actor by the Viewers for Quality Television.

To achieve Vincent's fearsome look, Perlman spends the first hours of each shooting day in the makeup artist's chair. He has traveled this road before. His first starring movie role in *Quest for Fire*, required extensive makeup. Shot on the frozen bogs of Scotland, Perlman spent eight months barefoot and almost naked portraying a prehistoric Ulam tribesman. And later in the film of *The Name of the Rose*, he again spent hours being transformed into the deformed and hunchbacked monk Salvatore.

Perlman now lives in Los Angeles with his wife, fashion designer Opal Stone, and their four-and-a-half year old daughter, Blake Amanda.

Linda Hamilton stars as Catherine Chandler, the beautiful and strong-willed attorney who renounces her place in Manhattan society to become an investigator for the New York District Attorney's office.

Linda was born on September 26 in Salisbury, Maryland. She has an older sister, and identical twin sister (who is a registered nurse), and a younger brother. Hamilton became involved in acting as a child, working with children's theater groups and later studied for two years at Washington College in Maryland, after which she moved to New York to study acting. She attended workshops at the Lee Strasberg Theater Institute, and also studied with Nicholas Ray. Linda made her professional bow on the daytime television drama *Search for Tomorrow*.

In the summer of 1979, she moved to Hollywood. Widely recognized for her performance in *The Terminator*, Hamilton has also starred in *Black Moon Rising*, *Children of the Corn*, in the made-for-television movies, *Rape and Marriage: The Rideout Case*, *Toward the Light*, and *Secret Weapons*, in addition to guest appearances on *Hill Street Blues*. During the filming of *T.A.G. — The Assassination Game*, she met Bruce Abbot, a fellow actor playing the psychopath trying to kill her on camera. Off camera, they were married on December 19, 1982. She and her husband make their home in Los Angeles.

Roy Dotrice stars as Father, the brilliant recluse who has given up life Above for a home in the hidden tunnels beneath New York.

A native of England, Dotrice did not even consider acting until his capture at age 16 in World War II. During his three-and-a-half year internment at Stalag Luft III, he played the role of Mio in Maxwell Anderson's *"Winterset."*

After the war, Dotrice acted in and/or directed over 500 repertory productions, before joining the Royal Shakespeare Company in 1959. There he performed with Laurence Olivier, Charles Laughton, John Gielgud, Paul Scofield, and Paul Robeson, while starting a baseball team with his fellow troupe members.

A veteran of stages in London, Stratford, and on Broadway, Dotrice received a Tony nomination for his work in *"A Life."* He has more than a dozen films to his credit, including the role of Leopold Mozart in *Amadeus*, and television credits such as *"Mister Lincoln," "Dickens of London," "Family Reunion,"* the Emmy Award-winning *"The Caretaker"* and *"Brief Lives"* for which he was voted Actor of the Year in 1968.

Married for 42 years to actress Kay Newman, Dotrice and his wife have three daughters, all actresses. He and his wife keep homes in both London and Los Angeles.

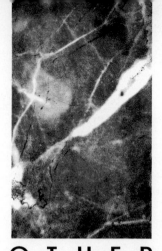

OTHER FINE BOOKS FROM FIRST

T·R·A·D·E P·A·P·E·R·B·A·C·K·S
F O R   C H I L D R E N

The Enchanted Apples of Oz ($7.95)

The Secret Island of Oz ($7.95)

The Ice King of Oz ($7.95)

The Forgotten Forest of Oz ($8.95)

F O R   A L L   A G E S

Beowulf ($6.95)

Elric of Melniboné ($14.95)

Elric: Sailor on the Seas of Fate ($14.95)

Hawkmoon: The Jewel in the Skull ($9.95)

Hexbreaker: A Badger Graphic Novel ($8.95)

Lone Wolf and Cub Deluxe Edition ($19.95)

The Original Nexus ($7.95)

Teenage Mutant Ninja Turtles®, Books 1-4, ($9.95each)

Coming in February 1990: Classics Illustrated.

F O R   M A T U R E   R E A D E R S

American Flagg!: Hard Times ($11.95)

American Flagg!: Southern Comfort ($11.95)

American Flagg!: State of the Union ($11.95)

Team Yankee ($12.95)

Olivia Calender 1990 ($9.95) Available in August 1989.

C·O·M·I·C   M·A·G·A·Z·I·N·E·S

Badger ($1.95)

Dreadstar ($1.95)

Grimjack ($1.95)

Lone Wolf and Cub ($2.95)

Nexus ($1.95)

Sable ($1.95)

Whisper ($1.95)

First Publishing graphic novels, comics, and other products are available in finer bookstores and all comic retail stores throughout the country. To order individual trade paperbacks send cover price plus $1.50 for postage and handling; or for further information about comic magazine subscriptions write to: First Publishing, 435 N. LaSalle Street, Chicago, IL 60610.